It's Easy To Play
Classical Ch

Wise Publications
part of The Music Sales Group

London / New York / Paris / Sydney / Copenhagen / Berlin / Madrid / Tokyo

Published by
Wise Publications
14-15 Berners Street, London W1T 3LJ, UK.

Exclusive Distributors:
Music Sales Limited
Distribution Centre, Newmarket Road, Bury St Edmunds, Suffolk IP33 3YB, UK.
Music Sales Pty Limited
120 Rothschild Avenue, Rosebery, NSW 2018, Australia.

Order No. AM988790
ISBN 13: 978-84609-863-5
ISBN 10: 1-84609-863-7
This book © Copyright 2006 by Wise Publications.

Compiled and edited by Jessica Williams.
Cover illustration by Liz Barrand.
Music arranged by Derek Jones.
Music processed by Paul Ewers Music Design.
Printed in the the EU.

Your Guarantee of Quality
As publishers, we strive to produce every book to the highest commercial standards.
The music has been freshly engraved and the book has been carefully designed to
minimise awkward page turns and to make playing from it a real pleasure.
Particular care has been given to specifying acid-free, neutral-sized paper made from
pulps which have not been elemental chlorine bleached.
This pulp is from farmed sustainable forests and was produced with special regard for the environment.
Throughout, the printing and binding have been planned to ensure a sturdy,
attractive publication which should give years of enjoyment.
If your copy fails to meet our high standards, please inform us and we will gladly replace it.

www.musicsales.com

'Adagietto' from Symphony No.5

(Fourth Movement)

Composed by Gustav Mahler

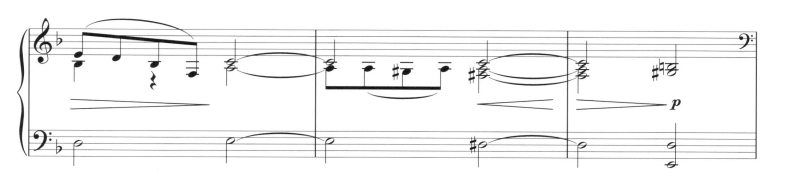

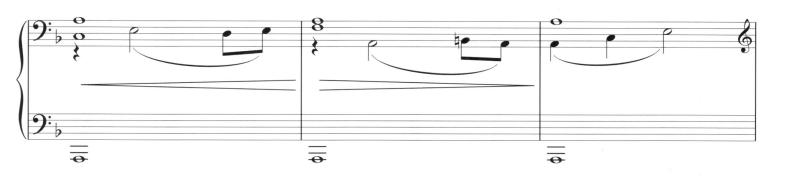

Adagio For Strings, Op.11

Composed by Samuel Barber

Any Other Name

(from 'American Beauty')

Composed by Thomas Newman

Canon in D

Composed by Johann Pachelbel

13

Clair de Lune
(from 'Suite Bergamasque')

Composed by Claude Debussy

Andante espressivo

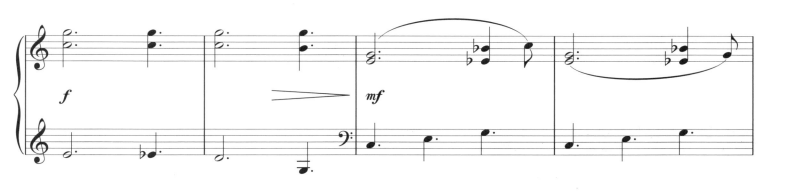

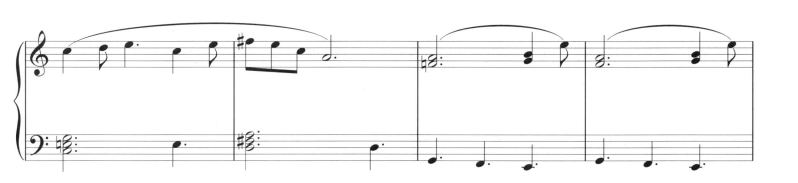

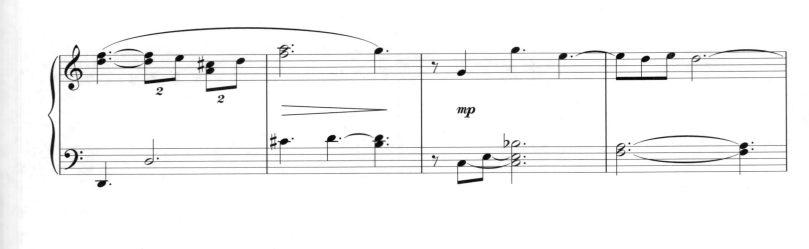

Hoppípolla

(featured in the TV series 'Planet Earth')

Words & Music by Jon Birgisson, Orri Dryasson, Georg Holm & Kjartan Sveinsson

Eternal Vow
(from 'Crouching Tiger, Hidden Dragon')

Composed by Tan Dun

Freely ♩ = 120

Con pedale

Into The West

(from 'The Lord Of The Rings: The Return Of The King')

Words & Music by Annie Lennox, Howard Shore & Fran Walsh

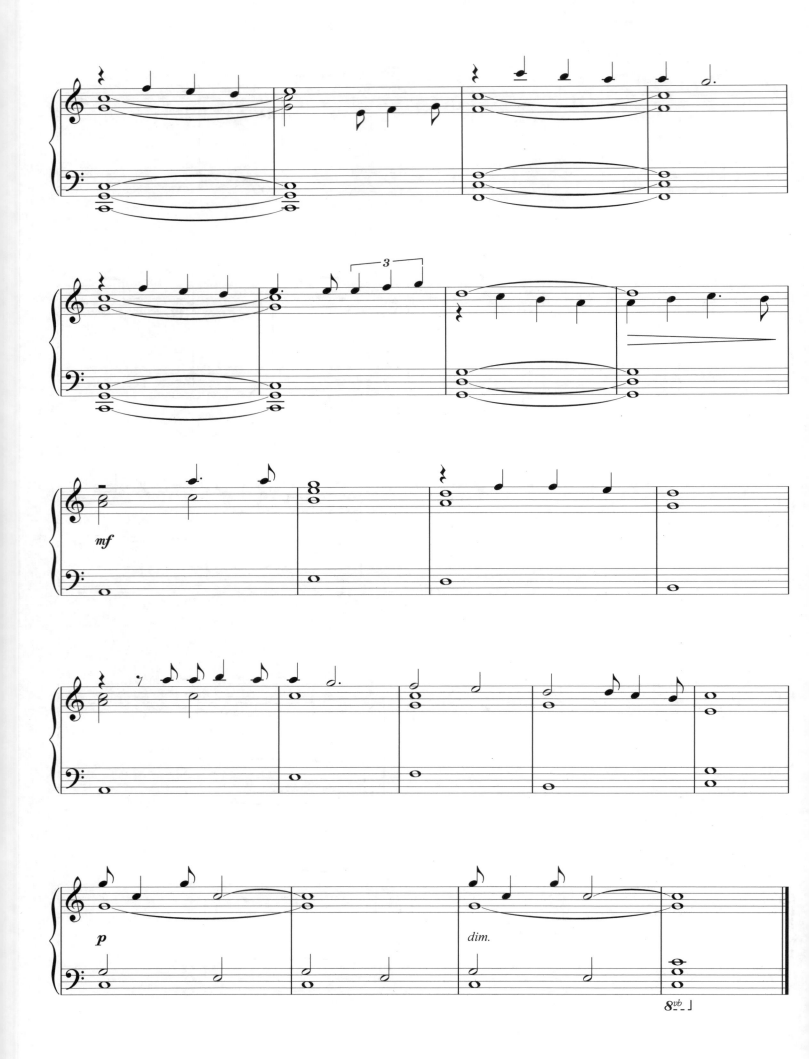

Le Onde

Composed by Ludovico Einaudi

27

Miserere

Composed by Gregorio Allegri

Pie Jesu

(from 'Requiem, Op.48')

Composed by Gabriel Fauré

Panis Angelicus

Composed by César Franck

35

Schindler's List

Composed by John Williams

Six Feet Under
(Theme)

Composed by Thomas Newman

Sky
(from 'The Bluebird Variations')

Composed by Patrick Hawes

The Swan

Composed by Camille Saint-Saëns

To A Wild Rose

Composed by Edward MacDowell

Weather Storm

Music by Craig Armstrong, Nellee Hooper,
Grantley Marshall, Andrew Vowles & Robert Del Naja

1/08(64514)